Amazing Animals

Super Safari

First published 2009 by Macmillan Children's Books
a division of Macmillan Publishers Limited
20 New Wharf Road, London N1 9RR
Basingstoke and Oxford
Associated companies throughout the world
www.panmacmillan.com

ISBN: 978-0-230-74372-4 (HB)
ISBN: 978-0-330-50988-6 (PB)

Text copyright © Tony Mitton 2009
Illustrations copyright © Ant Parker 2009
Moral rights asserted.
Consultancy by David Burnie

1 3 5 7 9 8 6 4 2

A CIP catalogue record for this book is available from the British Library.

Printed in China

To Lauren Austin next door.
With best wishes - TM
For Bruno and Polar Cub - AP

Amazing Animals
Super Safari

Tony Mitton and Ant Parker

MACMILLAN CHILDREN'S BOOKS

In Africa the grassy plains
are vast and dry and hot.

They're teeming with wild animals.
There really are a lot!

Here's a herd of elephants.
They're bulky, big and grey.

And yet they seem so gentle
as they wander on their way.

A happy hippopotamus
lies lolling in a pool.

The mud and water keep its skin
so smooth and moist and cool.

The zebra and the antelope
seem peaceful side by side.

Yet as they graze they're wary
of the nearby lion pride.

The lions look so scary.
They hunt to get their meat.

But only when they're hungry
and they need some food to eat.

A group of tall giraffe are browsing,
heads up in the sky.

Their long necks reach the treetops,
where luscious leaves grow high.

Rhinoceroses have two horns
and skin that's very thick.

If they start to charge you,
you'd better back off - quick!

The cheetah chases antelopes.
It's spotted, lean and fast.

No creature sprints as swiftly.
Just see it speeding past.

Baboon troops go out foraging
for tasty grassland snacks.

The little babies ride upon
their busy parents' backs.

We've seen some grassland creatures
on our trip across the plain.

You might just spot some others
if you make the trip again.

Did you spot . . .

the leopard?

the kori bustard?

the wildebeest?

the vulture?

the meerkats?

the crocodile?

the ostriches?

the oxpeckers?

the warthogs?